THE BABY
BEAST

For Juno

First published in Great Britain in 2019 by Andersen Press Ltd.,

20 Vauxhall Bridge Road, London SW1V 2SA.

Copyright © Chris Judge, 2019

The right of Chris Judge to be identified as the

author and illustrator of this work has been

asserted by him in accordance with the

Copyright, Designs and Patents Act, 1988.

All rights reserved.

Printed and bound in Malaysia.

1   3   5   7   9   10   8   6   4   2

British Library Cataloguing in Publication Data available.

ISBN 978 1 78344 776 3

THE BABY
BEAST

CHRIS JUDGE

Andersen Press

One fine, spring morning, the Beast opened his front door to get his newspaper...

... but discovered a surprise waiting for him. It looked like an egg. The Beast had never been given an egg before.

"How do you look after an egg?" the Beast wondered.

First he tried sharing some of his breakfast.

Then he took it for a nice long walk.

But the egg didn't seem to be enjoying itself at all.

Doing his chores, the Beast forgot about the egg...

... and lost it!

Almost.

When someone knocked on the door during bathtime, the Beast forgot about the egg again...

... and dropped it! (Ouch.)

He really was awful at looking after eggs. To say sorry, the Beast took the egg on a trek up his favourite mountain.

But when they stopped for lunch, things did not go according to plan.

It rolled straight into the emergency room.
Luckily Dr Yoko was an expert on eggs.*

*Officially called an eggspert.

"You must follow these instructions," said
Dr Yoko. "You won't have to wait long."

The Beast read the instructions carefully.

LOOKING AFTER

1. Keep it warm
- Heating needs to be high
- Egg needs to be wrapped up
- Nest needs to be snuggly and soft

2. Turn your egg
Turn your egg every four hours to make sure it is heated evenly

YOUR FIRST EGG

3. Play soft music (nothing too loud)

4. Give it lots of love

5. Wait

It all seemed clear except for one thing: "What am I waiting for?" wondered the Beast.

The Beast bought all the things he would need,
plus some things he wouldn't...

Then he carried all his new things home.

When everything was ready, the only thing left to do was wait.
(It had been a long day.)

The next morning, the Beast opened his shed
door to see the egg and got a nasty surprise.
The shed had been burgled!

"Oh, Egg!" sobbed the Beast. "You were heavy and you were hard work and you were often incredibly annoying, but I loved you."

And that was when something wonderful happened.

The Beast realised what (or rather who) he had been waiting for.

Dr Yoko was very pleased. The Beast had done a wonderful job. Now instead of a list of instructions she gave him a whole book to learn how to look after Baby Beast.

At first it seemed like really hard work,
and the Beast had a few setbacks.

But after a while

he seemed to get the hang of it.

The Beast's favourite time was the end of the day, because they both loved bedtime stories.

"Good night, sleep tight Baby Beast," he whispered, thinking how sometimes the biggest surprises are the best.

THE BOOK OF
CANDLES

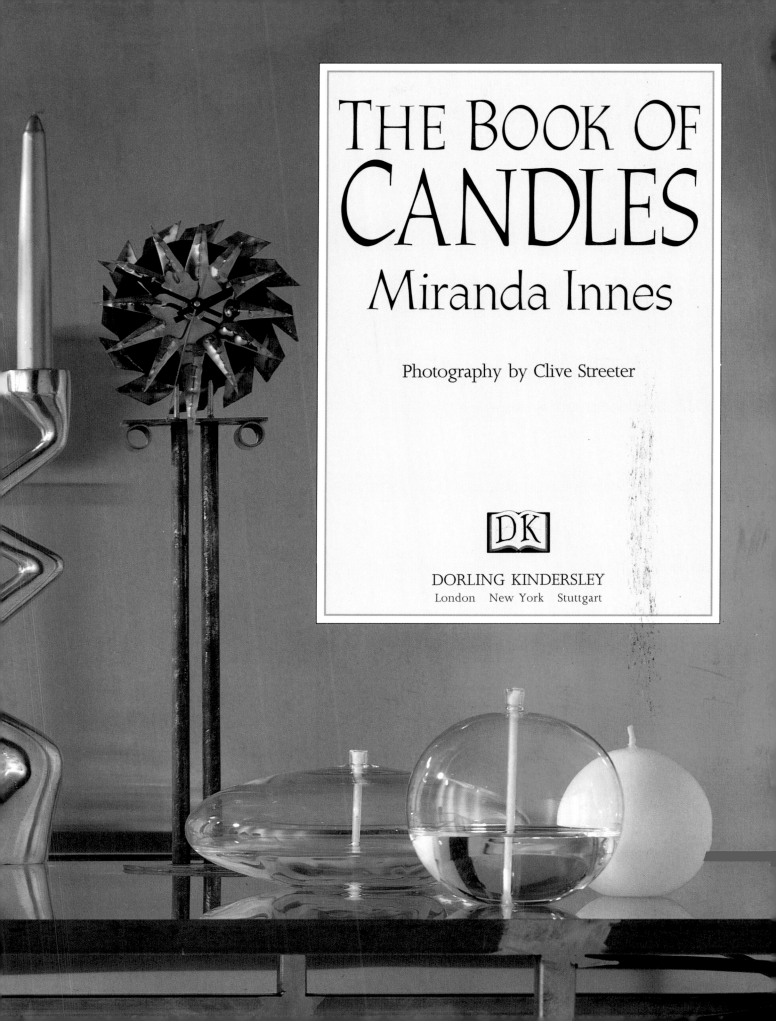

THE BOOK OF CANDLES

Miranda Innes

Photography by Clive Streeter

DK

DORLING KINDERSLEY

London   New York   Stuttgart

To Will, Leo and Roger

A DORLING KINDERSLEY BOOK

Art editor Sarah Scrutton
Project editor Claire Le Bas

Art director Anne-Marie Bulat
Managing editor Daphne Razazan

Production controller Deborah Wehner

First published in Great Britain in 1991
by Dorling Kindersley Limited,
9 Henrietta Street, London WC2E 8PS

A CIP catalogue record for this book is
available from the British Library.

ISBN 0-8.6318-645-9

Reproduced by J. Film, Singapore
Printed and bound by Kyodo, Singapore

CONTENTS

INTRODUCTION

Music-making
Players perform by
candlelight in
The Concert by
Hendrick ter Brugghen.

Candles create instant atmosphere – their glow makes an intimate and comforting sphere, with a touch of romance and a sense of warmth. There is something about the flickering golden flame that transforms a humble supper into *dîner à deux* – the enchanted circle of light encourages people to look at each other afresh, to appreciate and listen with long-forgotten fascination.

Until the convenient, but somewhat less romantic, virtues of paraffin and gas were discovered, it was by candlelight that books were written, songs sung, passions kindled, and weddings celebrated. Julius Caesar made plans by candlelight, Dante worshipped Beatrice, Shakespeare pondered his Dark Lady, Caravaggio painted Bacchus. Churches exhaled the sweet smell of beeswax, and the streets of Pepys's London were rank with the stench of tallow candles.

A powerful focus
The bright, steady flame has an almost hypnotic effect in this painting of *Christ before the High Priest* by Gerrit van Honthorst.

The little flame was the emblem of hope, life, truth, virtue, wisdom, and in religious observance, of the love of God. At Candlemas, all the candles to be used in the church in the coming year are blessed, in remembrance of the presentation of Jesus in the temple, when the aged Simeon addressed Christ as the Light of the World.

Rushlights and the much reviled tallow candles were the only recourse of the poor until the 19th century. The slaughter of one bullock provided enough tallow for three years' worth of candles, and a well-organized household would produce 300 or so at a candle-making session. In 13th-century Paris, the members of a guild of tallow chandlers went from house to house making candles. In the 15th century, the sieur de Brez of Paris revolutionized the business by inventing the candle mould. Beeswax resisted the new-fangled mould, and until this century, with the discovery of silicon releasing-agents, it has always been shaped by dipping. In France and Britain, the Guild of Wax Chandlers was created to protect beeswax workers from taint by association with their tallow-chandler brethren.

In a particularly punitive piece of British legislation, candles were taxed in 1709, and people were forbidden from making their own. This progressively more stringent tax was finally repealed in 1831, resulting in a renaissance of decorative candles. But it was not

Street market
Candlelight casts a glow over the wares in *The Gamestall* by Petras van Schendel.

7

until almost too late, when more convenient alternatives were on the horizon, that a Frenchman, M. Chevreul, purified tallow by treating it with alkali and sulphuric acid, and thereby producing the clean-burning, long-lasting stearin candle.

Another Frenchman, M. Cambaceres, came up with the plaited wick in 1825, which he pickled in mineral salts to make it curve on burning, thus obviating all the fussy necessities of wick trimming, and the familiar unpleasantness of smoke. Joseph Morgan created a candle-making machine in 1834, which could turn out 1,500 candles an hour, and two years later, a palm oil substance, palmatine, was patented as an alternative to existing waxes. In the mid-19th century, candle-making companies owned coco-palm plantations in Sri Lanka, and could produce a hundred tons of candles weekly. In 1850, paraffin wax appeared and in 1857, in combination with stearin and the plaited wick, it finally resulted in bright, affordable candles. This precisely coincided with the sudden availability of cheap paraffin lamps: the candle was eclipsed.

But from the very beginning, ingenuity was busy with this essential article. Alfred the Great devised a solution to the all too easily extinguished flame, consisting of a thin shield of horn to protect it against draughts. A thousand years ago, the candle-clock was invented, which marked the hours, somewhat inaccurately,

Making candles
Molten wax was scooped up from the vat and poured over the suspended wicks until they were the desired diameter.

Letter to a loved one
From an early advertisement, *Soldier Boy*, for Price's Candles.

by burning a candle with 12 horizontal lines painted on its side. In 17th-century England, bidding at an auction was conducted to the light of an inch-high candle – when it guttered out, bidding closed.

These days, barring power-cuts, candles have no other function than to give pleasure and to provide a nostalgic alternative light-source. The smooth glossiness of machine-made candles, the fragrance of beeswax, the sweetness of scented candles make them lovely objects in themselves. They are the cheapest piece of theatre – a couple of red candles and a pine branch make an instant Christmas; a

Romantic lanterns
Lighting paper lanterns with tapers in *Carnation, Lily, Lily, Rose* by John Singer Sargent.

bouquet of white roses with sugar-pink candles creates romantic seclusion; tall wrought iron candle-sticks holding beeswax cylinders have the swashbuckling bravado of The Three Musketeers. It is surprising what you can do with wax and string.

A CATALOGUE OF CANDLES & CANDLESTICKS

From the simplest and most utilitarian candles with their plain intrinsic beauty, to the glittering prisms of the most sophisticated and intricately wrought candelabra, this is a sourcebook for the essential elements of candle power, illustrating the huge diversity of colours and shapes, decoration and finishes available – inspiration for making your own candles at home and an indispensable buyer's guide.

Dipped candles

The oldest method of candle-making, dipping involves repeatedly immersing a wick in molten wax until enough layers accumulate to form a candle of the desired width. The technique has been used since Roman times, when a slim roll of papyrus was dipped into beeswax bleached by the sun. Dipped candles usually come in pairs with concentric rings of wax in section like the rings on a tree trunk. They have a tapered shape and an uneven base, with a loop of wick between the pair making a "handle" for dipping into the vat of molten wax.

Traditional dipped
Old-fashioned elegance combines with an odourless, clean flame in these candles made of paraffin wax.

Wick forming a handle for dipping

16.5cm
(6½in) pair

20cm
(8in) pair

30cm
(12in) pair

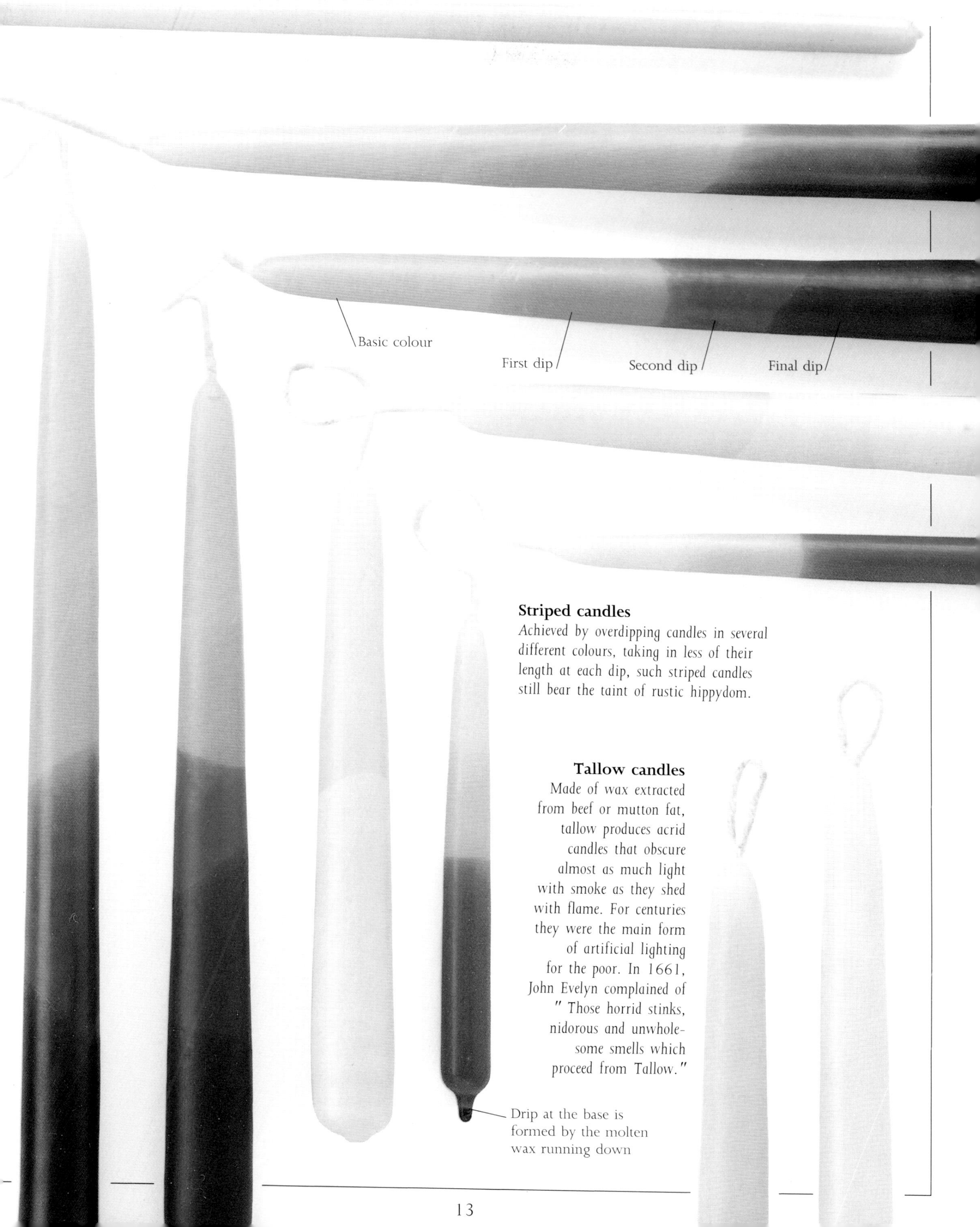

Basic colour

First dip

Second dip

Final dip

Striped candles

Achieved by overdipping candles in several different colours, taking in less of their length at each dip, such striped candles still bear the taint of rustic hippydom.

Tallow candles

Made of wax extracted from beef or mutton fat, tallow produces acrid candles that obscure almost as much light with smoke as they shed with flame. For centuries they were the main form of artificial lighting for the poor. In 1661, John Evelyn complained of " Those horrid stinks, nidorous and unwhole-some smells which proceed from Tallow."

Drip at the base is formed by the molten wax running down

Church candles

The unselfconscious legacy of ancient tradition, church candles have survived almost unchanged for centuries. Symbolizing purity, life, the soul, the unquenchable light of faith and the love of God for man, they are an essential element in religious ceremonies throughout the world. Traditionally made with a high proportion of beeswax, church candles are available from many candle shops, and have the classic simplicity that looks good in any setting.

Processional tapers

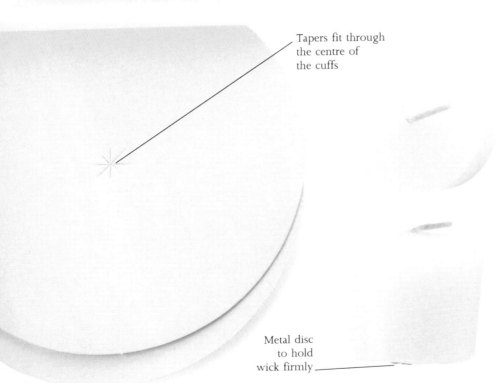

Tapers fit through the centre of the cuffs

Metal disc to hold wick firmly

Tapers and cuffs
Paper cuffs around slender processional tapers prevent drips of wax burning the hands of those holding them.

Votum candles
Placed in a side-chapel in a red or blue glass container, these burn constantly and slowly in remembrance of the dead.

Votive candles
These are lit by the laity to solemnize a prayer, and burn in serried ranks on stands consisting of 21 or 36 prickets.

45cm (18in) altar candle

23cm (9in)
altar candle

16.5cm ($6^{1}/_{2}$in)
altar candle

15cm (6in)
altar
candle

16.5cm ($6^{1}/_{2}$in)
septalite

Altar candles (above and below)
*Varying in length from 15cm (6in) to almost a metre
(3ft), these stand in magnificent candlesticks flanking
the altar, and are lit for the duration of a service.*

Septalite (above)
*A very grand and somewhat more convenient
votum light than the little side-chapel versions,
septalites burn for a full seven days.*

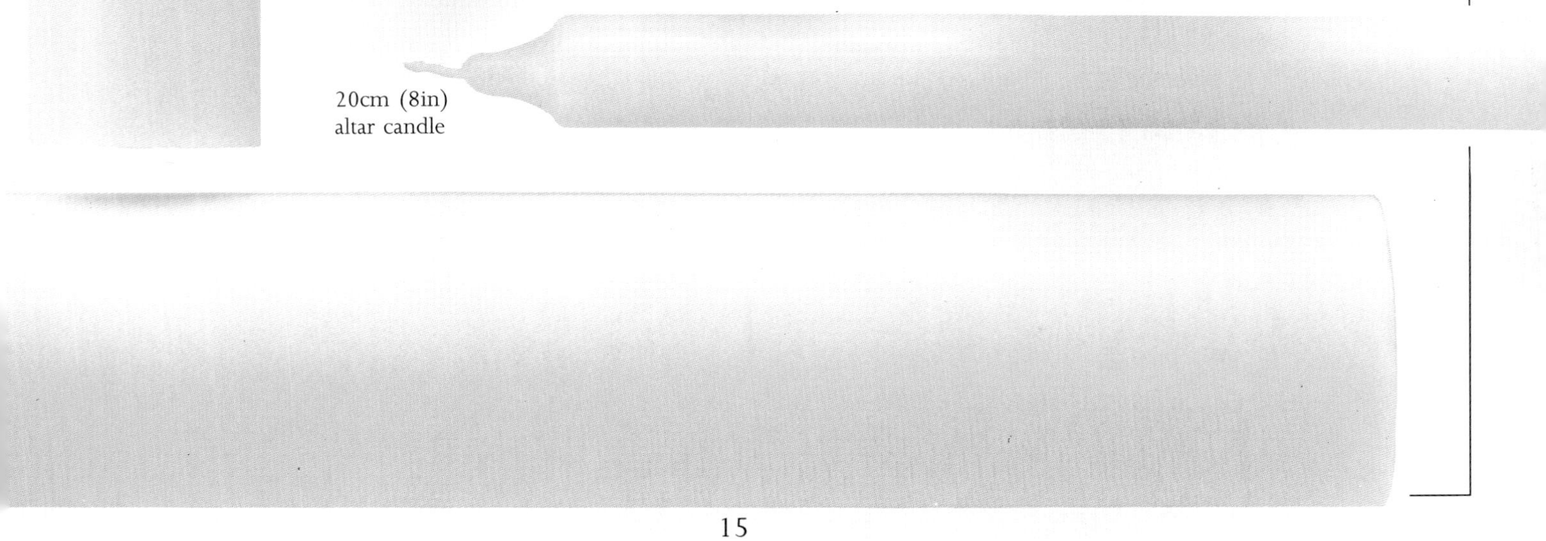

20cm (8in)
altar candle

Beeswax candles

Simplest and best, beeswax candles are the most precious, burning slowly and clearly with a wonderful honey fragrance. Beeswax is difficult to mould, and the classic production method involves dipping – an expensive and time-consuming business. Producing honeycomb is labour-intensive for the bees too, so nowadays beekeepers give them a headstart by providing a ready-made base for the wax honeycomb.

Dipped beeswax
The classic tapered cylinder.

Moulded beeswax
Wax can be moulded into any shape, but simplicity best suits the qualities of beeswax.

Moulded skep - a very refined sort of pun

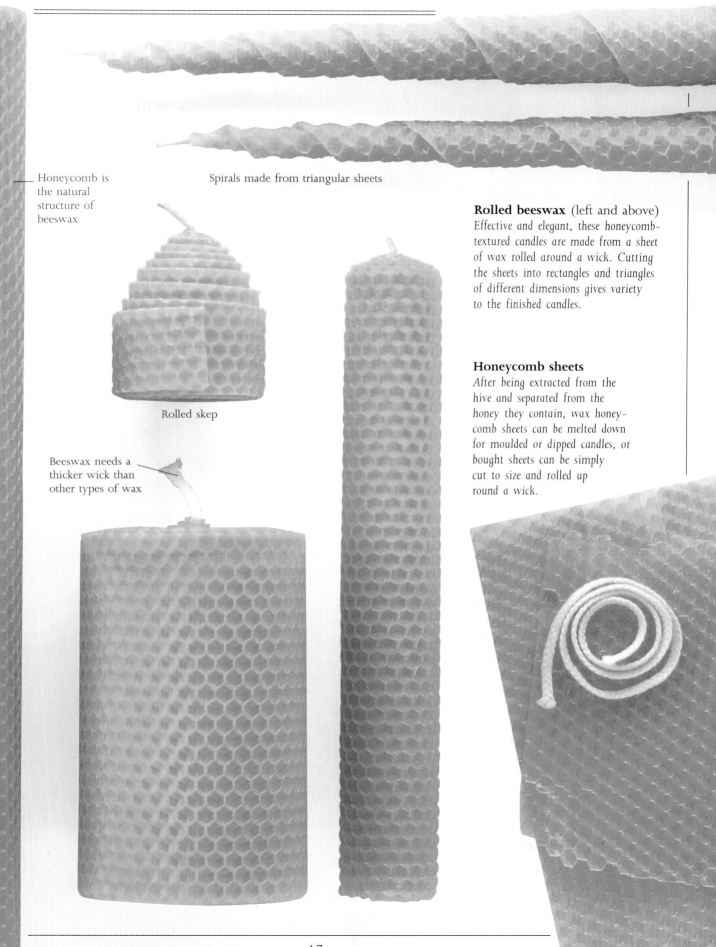

Spirals made from triangular sheets

Honeycomb is the natural structure of beeswax

Rolled skep

Beeswax needs a thicker wick than other types of wax

Rolled beeswax (left and above)
Effective and elegant, these honeycomb-textured candles are made from a sheet of wax rolled around a wick. Cutting the sheets into rectangles and triangles of different dimensions gives variety to the finished candles.

Honeycomb sheets
After being extracted from the hive and separated from the honey they contain, wax honeycomb sheets can be melted down for moulded or dipped candles, or bought sheets can be simply cut to size and rolled up round a wick.

Christmas candles

There is a natural affinity between candles and Christmas time, which goes back to pagan midwinter solar observances: the turning point of the year at its darkest nadir celebrated defiantly with lights and evergreens. From the north and Celtic culture came yuletide expressed in the candle-decked Christmas tree, later popularized by Prince Albert; and, with a Christian admixture of symbolic fires and lights, we end up with the unbeatable classic combination of glowing red, green and gold candles.

Moulded candle overdipped in gold

Advent candle
The twenty-four holy days of Advent are marked by burning one section each day.

Decorated candles
Every aspect of Christmas finds exuberant expression in wax — trees, angels, St. Nicholas, the star of Bethlehem.

Plasticized glaze for a shiny finish

Moulded tassel

Applied glitter

Painted colours

Moulded star

Tree candle (right) For a traditional touch, decorate the tree with candles; fix them securely in clip-on holders, and never leave them unattended.

Classic spiral

Gold thread spiral

Snow-flake of applied wax

Moulded column

Holly leaf transfer

Ribbon of applied wax

A rainbow of lights

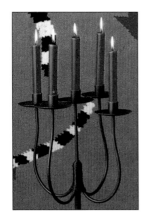

Lit or unlit, candles are pure, clear colour, available in a spectrum of harmonizing shades which are a decorator's dream, and which echo and reflect any kind of interior design. They look marvellous grouped, with toning colours side by side. Subtle partnerships can be made with candlesticks: use rich warm colours dappled with gold to reflect the opulence of a gilded baroque candlestick, or steely grey to give a metallic echo to pewter. Candles are the cheap, replaceable equivalent of fashion accessories, and the colours are there to be enjoyed — tall fondant pink tapers, cool Scandinavian blues and greens, glowing reds and yellows.

Blues and greens
Sky and sea, leaves and spring flowers — these are the colours of nature, equally at home with both pale rustic wood and the milky blue droplets of Venetian glass candelabra.

Creams and yellows
Celebrate spring with candles in fresh, sunny colours surrounded by terracotta pots of primroses.

Pinks
Sunrise, apple blossom, sugar mice — pink is the colour of innocence and youth, particularly in combination with white lilies and irises.

Reds
Shining strawberries, glittering garnets and rubies, fire and flame — reds signify warmth and passion, richness and luxury, and create an instant festive look.

Candle shapes

As everyone knows who has been unable to resist fiddling with melting candle wax, part of the allure of candles is their sculptural quality – moulded, carved or twisted, they can have the flawless smooth translucency of jade, or the ruggedly textured corrugations of a piece of farm equipment. Perfect spheres or intricate carved spirals, Father Christmas or shiny red hearts for St. Valentine's day, dark matt geometric shapes to cluster on a black lacquer tray in a stark modern interior, elegant spirals to grace Georgian silver candelabra – there are shapes to match every whim or style of decoration.

Figurative shapes
The jokier side of candle design – disposable kitsch for fun.

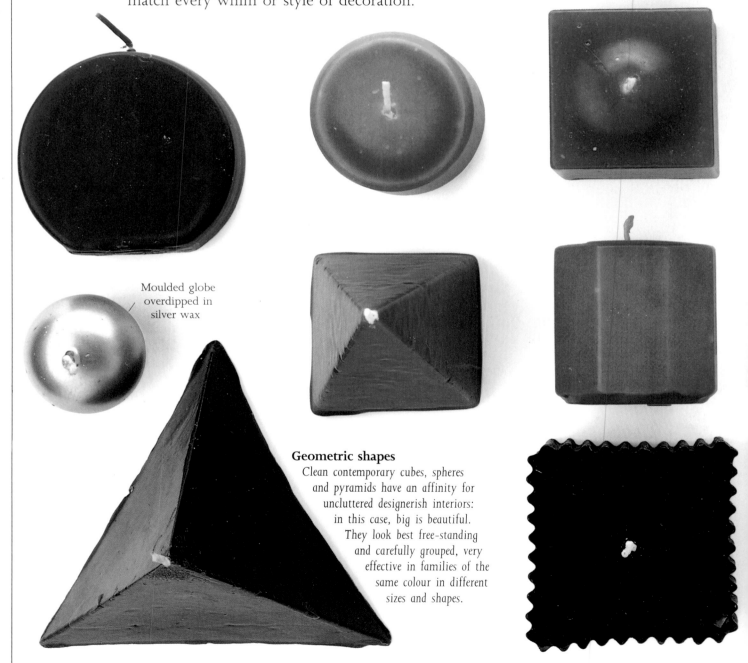

Moulded globe
overdipped in
silver wax

Geometric shapes
Clean contemporary cubes, spheres and pyramids have an affinity for uncluttered designerish interiors: in this case, big is beautiful. They look best free-standing and carefully grouped, very effective in families of the same colour in different sizes and shapes.

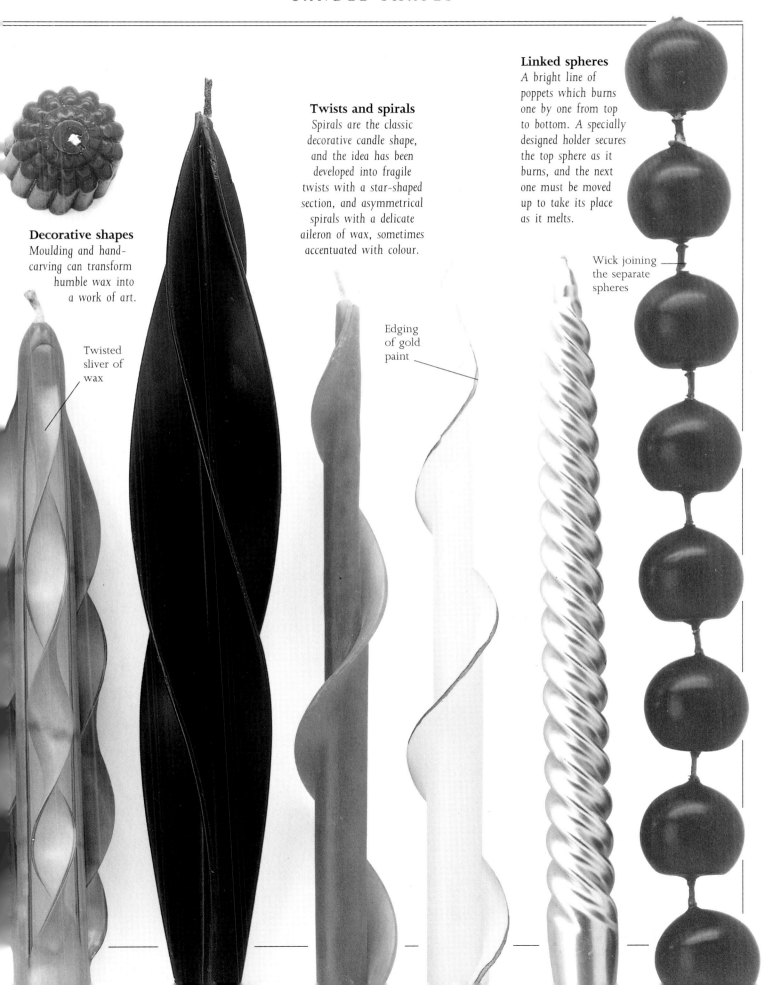

Linked spheres
A bright line of poppets which burns one by one from top to bottom. A specially designed holder secures the top sphere as it burns, and the next one must be moved up to take its place as it melts.

Twists and spirals
Spirals are the classic decorative candle shape, and the idea has been developed into fragile twists with a star-shaped section, and asymmetrical spirals with a delicate aileron of wax, sometimes accentuated with colour.

Decorative shapes
Moulding and hand-carving can transform humble wax into a work of art.

Twisted sliver of wax

Edging of gold paint

Wick joining the separate spheres

Decorated candles

There are no hard and fast rules to choosing decorated candles – the only guide is what you like, and what suits the context. Find candles to complement your possessions – a bold painted design echoes bright Provençal pottery, the fragile charm of pressed flower candles matches delicate Victorian porcelain, and the sumptuous richness of stippled and gilded candles looks well in an Art Nouveau setting.

Mottled finish (right)
A professional finish with a fine lacy veil of white wax over colour.

Simple hand-painted design

Marbled and streaked
Subtle swirls of blue and green are achieved by floating different coloured waxes in a dipping bath and immersing the candle briefly.

Sponged colours

Stencilled decoration

Paint finishes
Hand-painting has a naive charm, at home with peasant crockery. Sponged, stencilled and stippled candles vary from the bold to the sophisticated.

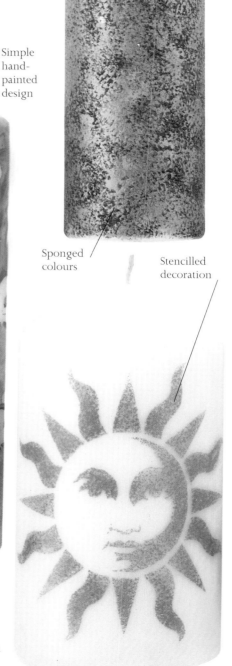

Stippled candle

Small flowers
and leaves
make pretty
decorations

Carved patterns

Pressed flowers
*Endowed with old-fashioned
charm, these candles are
perfect as presents.*

A bright mosaic
of rolled and
cut wax

Applied wax
*Tiny pieces of wax can be
attached to a candle with
wax glue. Surface decoration
can be as varied as the
imagination can concoct –
from a sprinkling of coloured
flecks to a delicate spiral of
twisted strands.*

Carved decorations
*Candles with an outer coating
of strong colour are carved to
reveal the white wax beneath.
These candles burn with a
lattice-like effect through
the dark exterior.*

Multi-coloured
*Covered with lozenges cut from rolls of wax overdipped in
bright colour, these candles glow like stained glass when lit.*

Scented and floating candles

As well as shedding a benign and flattering light, candles can also fill a room with fragrance – even unscented candles burn away noxious smells, and out of doors, citronella will keep mosquitos at a distance. The addition of perfume oil to a candle makes the wax more liquid, so most scented candles come in containers, or if free-standing, should be burned in a glass or jar that will hold the melted wax. There is a huge choice of fragrances, some of which are fresh and floral, some musky and oriental. What appeals to you is bound to be a highly personal matter – but choosing scented candles is one of life's more agreeable problems. Floating candles are often scented, their broad shape and the cool water preventing the molten wax spreading messily.

Refillable silver container

Free-standing candles
Made in a spectrum of colours, these look pretty in groups in pressed glass containers.

Candles in containers
The subtle simplicity of high-quality candles is enhanced by elegant containers of silver, glass or terracotta.

Dried flowers
Simple scented candles look good in plain terracotta or sand-coloured holders with a drift of dried flowers or pot pourri.

Floating candles
A flotilla of stars and flowers, their dancing lights reflected in water and on glass — floating candles are as hypnotic as firelight, and as romantic as Mediterranean harbour lights on a phosphorescent sea.

Float rose petals among the candles

Displaying the candles
Reflective bowls of faceted glass or metal make the most of floating candle flames. The water can be delicately tinted with food colouring, or sprinkled with small flowers, petals or even sequins. For safety, use a broad-based bowl with an outcurving lip.

Garden candles

Flares, lanterns and lamps, or terracotta pots filled with wax – candlelight is the most sympathetic of garden lighting, but it does require a little care and a generous supply of matches. In the Orient, paper lanterns are used to shield the flame from wind, and during the Catholic fiesta at Santa Fe, the streets are filled with celebrants bearing candles in stemmed goblets. At home, pathways and steps can be marked with flares or simply by standing a candle in sand in a small paper bag. For dining out of doors, a collection of nightlights in glasses or jars, and a storm lamp or two, are the most breeze-resistant lighting, and lanterns look pretty hung from trees.

Lanterns
Oriental pierced tin and brass lanterns make the candle flame twinkle like starlight. The indigenous variety is usually more utilitarian, traditionally consisting of an iron frame with glass or horn panels.

Flower pot candles
These burn slowly, and the multiple wicks are stout enough to withstand a breeze. They are simple to make at home, and look good in an old hand-made pot.

Traditional lantern

Outdoor candle

Decorative Egyptian lanterns

Garden flare

Outdoor candles and flares
Outdoor candles are chunky enough not to be blown over, a problem that is solved for flares by their long bamboo stalks, which can be pushed into the ground. Flares come in strong, bright colours and burn for three hours or more, depending on the strength of the wind.

Candle lamps

A cluster of candle lamps makes a
sparkling centre-piece to a dinner table.
The flame is protected from a breeze by
a globe or bowl of clear, etched or coloured
glass, very like the shade on paraffin lamps
for which these candle holders were the
precursor. There are hanging versions, too
– bell shapes in clear or green glass.

The glass bowl can
be lifted off the base

Storm lantern with
metal base for stability

Egyptian
storm lantern

Metal candlesticks

The classic material for candlesticks, metal can be worked into virtually any shape, from delicate filigree flowers to robust pillars. Antique metal candlesticks tend to survive longer than their more fragile ceramic and glass counterparts, becoming all the better for centuries of polishing and the odd dent. The 18th century was the apogee of candle power: elegant ormolu and silver candlesticks survive in large numbers. Nostalgia for the lively warmth of candlelight has caused a renaissance of the old designs, from Gothic wrought iron to traditional pewter, while experimentation with new methods and materials has introduced some entirely novel ideas.

Traditional candlesticks
Contemporary wrought iron and brass fashioned with prickets and cups, or integral snuffers, pay homage to the grace and simplicity of ancient designs. Irregularity is part of the charm. They are at home in cottage or condominium.

Classic style
Stately interpretations of antique designs in silver, gilt, brass and bronze are perfect for Georgian interiors.

Country style pewter

Floral silver-plate candlestick

Modern reproduction of traditional design

Classic silver candlestick

An unusual combination of ceramic and silver

Gilt animals and mythical figures are typical of the 18th century

Baroque outburst in the form of an exuberant silver frog

Chamber candlestick with integral snuffer

Tin holder with attached matchbox container

Modern designs

Candlesticks range from a Napoleonic wreath with a glass lens to magnify the candle flame, to a shiny brass and copper sunflower intended to be clamped to the bath and hold a soothing glass of something. Wire, verdigris and iron manifest peasant charm or audacious wit, following sinuous contortions or utter rectitude.

Classical wreath combining copper, iron and glass

Verdigris finish

Glass lens

Traditional twisted iron candlestick

The malleability of copper allows wayward eccentricity

Clock candlestick – a modern variation of the ancient candle timer

Sculptural form in resin and bronze

Clamp to attach holder to the bath

Candlestick of bent and twisted wire

Distressed copper holder

Ceramic candlesticks

Intricately patterned and delicately coloured candlesticks are a natural extension of the eclectic richness of our ceramic heritage – there are echoes of the Orient, of South America, India and the Mediterranean, there are unpredictable shiny glazes and demure Victorian sprigged transfers, hand-painted patterns and plain matt terracotta. Simple columnar designs withstand the firing process best, and a carefully controlled element of irregularity adds an eccentric charm to handcrafted candlesticks. Few antiques remain – most of those that survive come from 19th-century dressing-table sets – but there is an avalanche of brightly decorated contemporary imports.

Designer

Quirky, quaint and definitely unique, these are love or hate candlesticks. They have a surprising adaptability, and look well in both crooked cottage and crisp uncluttered architectural surroundings.

Ethnic

With no pretensions to being fine art, fluent hand-painting allied with strange and interesting local traditions – an elephants' head base, for example – gives these candlesticks personality. The best setting is one that plays up to their colour or provides a sympathetic ethnic context.

Antique elephant candlestick from China

Thai blue and white ware

Naive pottery from Portugal

Organic shapes by contemporary designers

Bold surface decoration

Classic columns
Restrained colours and an
unadorned, dignified shape –
these are candlesticks that
look good in any context, and
are an affordable pastiche of
Georgian silver.

Spongeware (below)
*An ancient method of transferring
designs to ceramics, spongeware
has a robust and rustic simplicity.
Once, the patterns were printed
with potato cuts, and modern
spongeware is not much more
sophisticated in method.*

Floral
*Pretty, delicate and very
feminine, dressing-table
candlesticks with tasteful
floral transfers look happiest
in a bedroom, adorning a
bedside table or mantelpiece.*

Floral
transfer

Fruit and flowers –
typical spongeware themes

Moulded garland
decoration

Square plinths
echo Georgian styles

Glass candlesticks

From the simplest column to the most ornate confection of twists and rainbow droplets, the transparency and sparkle of glass make it a natural partner to candlelight. A single handsome frosted glass candlestick looks good, but a whole crowd of rich rose-window colours and prismatic facets looks stunning. Classics are deeply cut crystal, glittering dark Bohemian glass, elaborately decorated Venetian glass from Murano, swirling opalescent Art Nouveau – or more affordable, though highly decorative, Victorian pressed glass.

Handcrafted

Glass is all things to all men: a liquid when molten and friable when hard, it lends itself to both sinuous twists and glinting shards.

Squares of glass stacked into glittering ziggurats

Blown glass

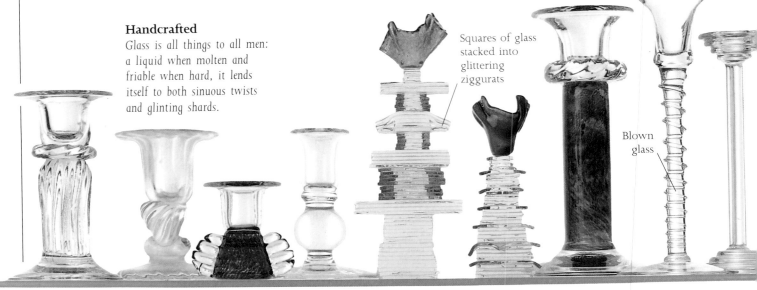

Coloured glass

Glass is the perfect medium for colour: both subtle and rich tones glow with pure intensity. Make the most of coloured glass by massing candlesticks together so that the light shines through them.

The ornate patterning was intended to disguise the seam on moulded glass

Moulded glass

Press-moulding is an ancient art, revived with a vengeance in the early 19th century. Recognizable by the raised seam where the edge of the mould was positioned, it often has a naive vigour and charm which make up for lack of pedigree.

Art Deco style pressed glass

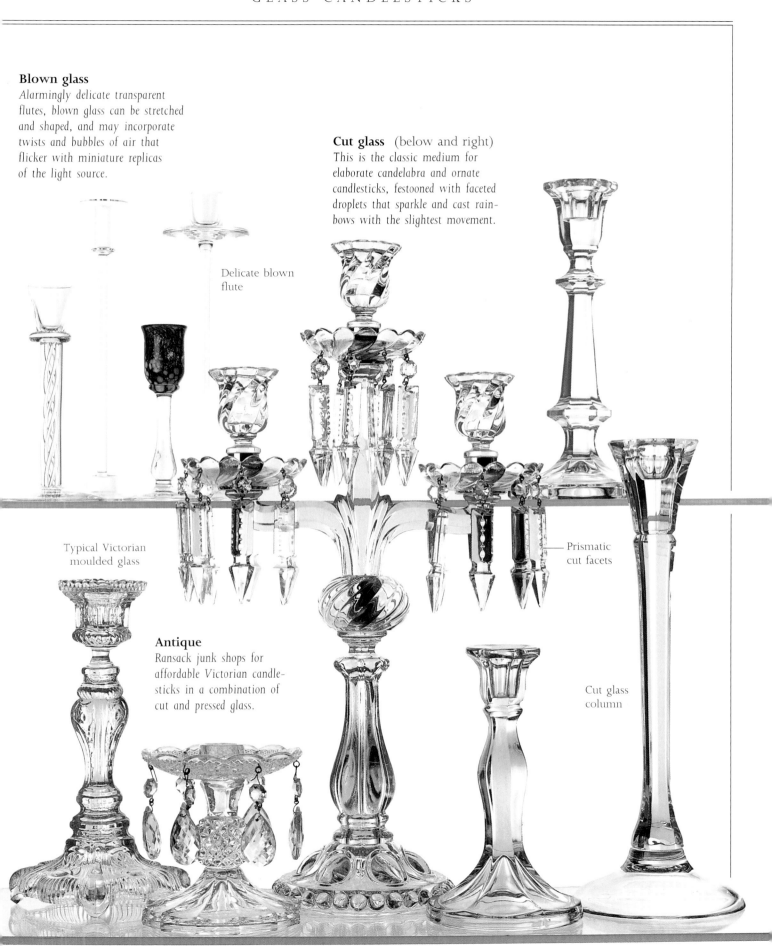

Blown glass
Alarmingly delicate transparent flutes, blown glass can be stretched and shaped, and may incorporate twists and bubbles of air that flicker with miniature replicas of the light source.

Cut glass (below and right)
This is the classic medium for elaborate candelabra and ornate candlesticks, festooned with faceted droplets that sparkle and cast rainbows with the slightest movement.

Delicate blown flute

Typical Victorian moulded glass

Prismatic cut facets

Antique
Ransack junk shops for affordable Victorian candlesticks in a combination of cut and pressed glass.

Cut glass column

Wooden candlesticks

Turned, painted, hand carved, or embellished with bands of brass or copper, wooden candlesticks tend to have a doughty solidity and somewhat masculine character. They are indirectly descended from the medieval expedient of supporting a candle with a spike in a block of wood, or several spikes (prickets) in a circular dished tray, attached to a wooden post or block – simple devices that persisted in country areas until the

19th century. More ornate wooden candlesticks were developed from the walnut, ebony and mahogany candle stands of the 17th and 18th centuries, which were often carved, painted or gilded, and pillar-shaped with a rise and fall action to allow for the candle burning down. The most magnificent wooden candlesticks are the monumental torchères, taller than a man, that used to illuminate castles and cathedrals.

Antique
Bobbin and barley-sugar turning are classic designs.

Pillars
Contemporary wooden candlesticks are often of simple design, relying on precision of craftsmanship and the natural quality of wood to give sophistication and elegance.

Paint finishes
Sponged, stippled or gilded, wooden candlesticks make a good subject for any paint effect.

Band of oxidized copper

Antique and modern dark wood in classic designs

Barley-sugar turned candlestick

Brass base

Ebony pillar

Dark paint with pale wood showing through

Ethnic

The most beautifully shaped and balanced candlesticks come from India — from tall and slender curvaceous baluster stems with decorative knops and touches of gilding, to huge open twist designs. They are sometimes painted in rich dark colours. Papier mâché too may be painted with a confetti of tiny flowers enhanced with bands of gold.

Carved wood

From India and Africa come carved candlesticks, washed with white to look like gesso, or finely turned from dark hardwood in whimsical designs like chess pieces.

Brass trim typical of Eastern candlesticks

Triple twist carved from a single piece of wood

Gesso-like effect

Ebony candlesticks from Africa

Carved and painted wood from India

Painted papier mâché from Kashmir

Turned, lacquered wood

Floorstanding candelabra

J ust the thing for a baronial manse, floorstanding candelabra add a touch of Gothic splendour to an interior. The grandest have always been made for religious purposes, from the seven-branched paschal candlesticks that traditionally mark Easter celebrations in church, to the huge candelabrum of Milan cathedral, known as the Trivulzio, which is 12 metres tall and embellished with flowers, people and monsters. Most are made of metal: an adaptable material, it can be as smooth as machine production can make it, or as characterfully rough-hewn as hand shaping can achieve.

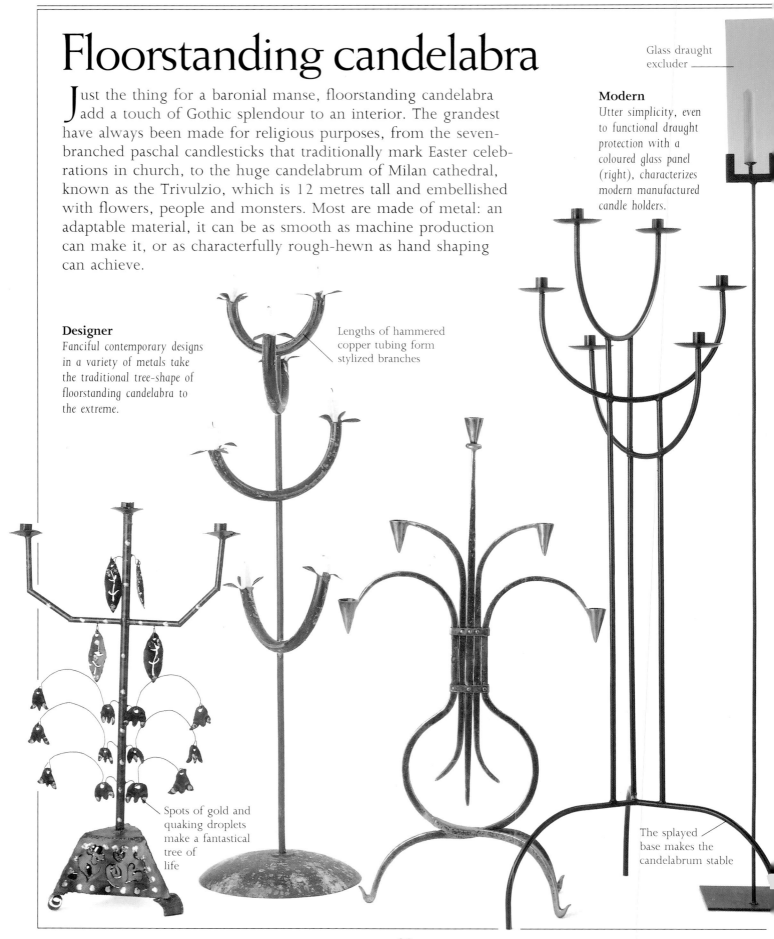

Glass draught excluder

Modern
Utter simplicity, even to functional draught protection with a coloured glass panel (right), characterizes modern manufactured candle holders.

Designer
Fanciful contemporary designs in a variety of metals take the traditional tree-shape of floorstanding candelabra to the extreme.

Lengths of hammered copper tubing form stylized branches

Spots of gold and quaking droplets make a fantastical tree of life

The splayed base makes the candelabrum stable

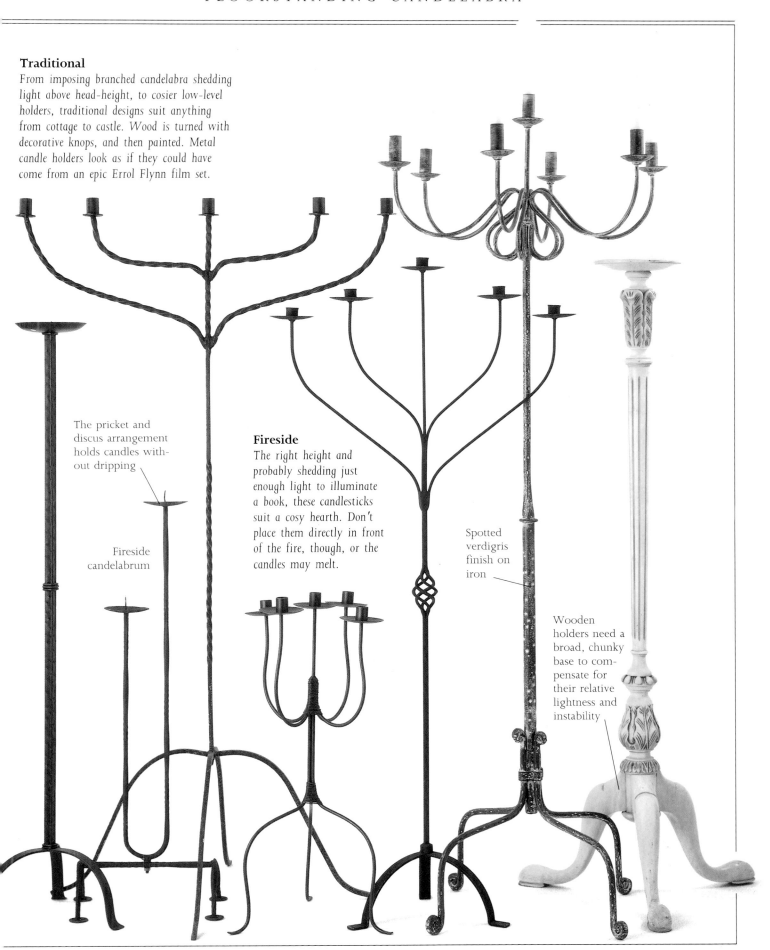

Traditional

From imposing branched candelabra shedding light above head-height, to cosier low-level holders, traditional designs suit anything from cottage to castle. Wood is turned with decorative knops, and then painted. Metal candle holders look as if they could have come from an epic Errol Flynn film set.

The pricket and discus arrangement holds candles without dripping

Fireside candelabrum

Fireside

The right height and probably shedding just enough light to illuminate a book, these candlesticks suit a cosy hearth. Don't place them directly in front of the fire, though, or the candles may melt.

Spotted verdigris finish on iron

Wooden holders need a broad, chunky base to compensate for their relative lightness and instability

Terracotta cherub

Sconces

W all sconces were the great discovery of the 17th century, and grand houses lined them up along their long dining halls. Initially they had reflectors of polished metal, usually silver, but gradually these were replaced with mirror glass, which reflected the flame more effectively. In the 18th century, mirror sconces were abandoned in favour of huge quantities of candles – the rich would have several dozen burning at once, held in rococo girandoles with picturesque details.

Nowadays there are sconces for every mood and style, from the most earthy ethnic to pinnacles of glittering refinement.

Mirrors
The standard expedient to multiply candle-power, mirrors and reflector plates of polished metal have been used since the 17th century.

Verdigris duck
A naive and perky folk motif inspired by Pennsylvanian Dutch domestic artefacts.

Indian
Divali sconce

Traditional
Tin and iron in simple, elegant shapes.

Ethnic
Divali, the Indian festival of lights, is celebrated with sconces portraying animals. The multi-storey pineapple is a new departure.

Shaker tin sconce

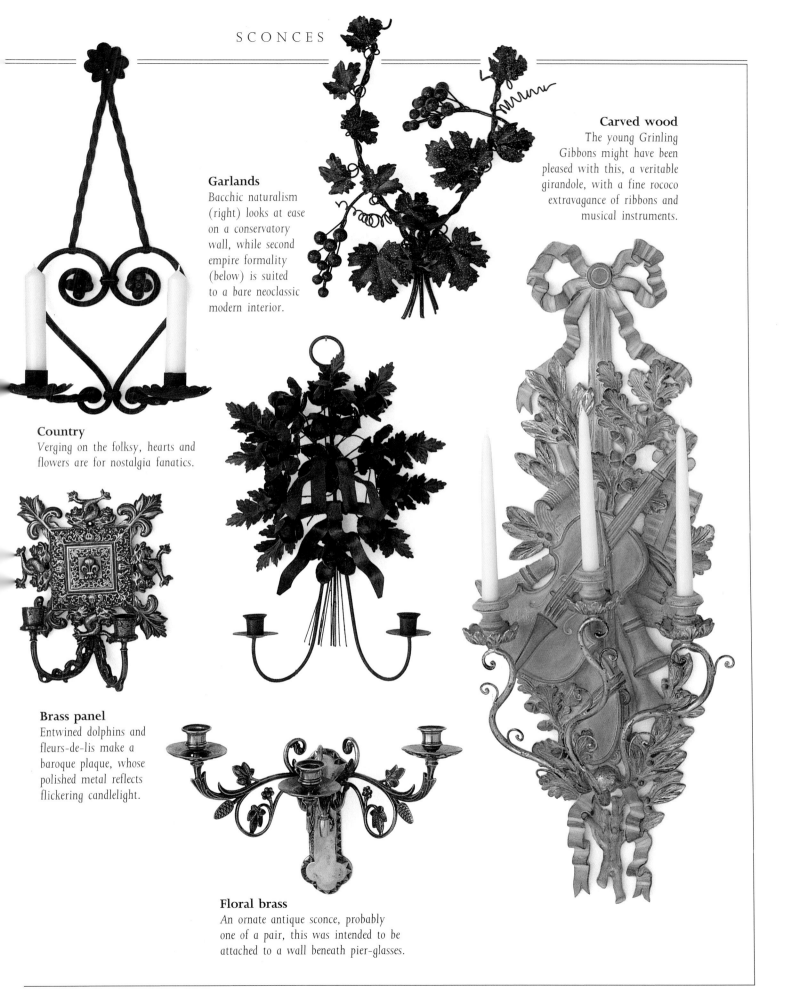

Garlands
Bacchic naturalism (right) looks at ease on a conservatory wall, while second empire formality (below) is suited to a bare neoclassic modern interior.

Carved wood
The young Grinling Gibbons might have been pleased with this, a veritable girandole, with a fine rococo extravagance of ribbons and musical instruments.

Country
Verging on the folksy, hearts and flowers are for nostalgia fanatics.

Brass panel
Entwined dolphins and fleurs-de-lis make a baroque plaque, whose polished metal reflects flickering candlelight.

Floral brass
An ornate antique sconce, probably one of a pair, this was intended to be attached to a wall beneath pier-glasses.

Chandeliers

In the 12th century, massive hoops of iron or bronze, with multiple prickets for holding candles, hung from the ceilings of churches. Two hundred years later, brass chandeliers were surmounted by angels or saints, and often decorated with Gothic crocketing. A rope and pulley allowed them to be lowered for lighting and snuffing. The 17th century saw the manufacture of chandeliers with eight or so S-shaped arms curving outwards from a central globe. Throughout the 18th century, increasingly decorative glass chandeliers were fashionable, culminating in the brilliant coloured and cut glass confections of Venice and Bohemia.

Provençal chandelier

Graceful simplicity in a swooping web of iron, a design that would adapt well to a beamed and whitewashed country setting, or an urban loft with a view of rooftops.

Traditional country

Simple curves topped by a nosegay of curlicues, eight cups and candle sockets to shed a respectable glow of light, while avoiding the concomitant drip of wax. It is essential that chandeliers have adequate drip trays, or that you use non-drip candles: no-one relishes hot wax in their hair.

Drip tray

Slender candles emphasize the sweeping curves of the chandelier

Use a strong chain, as chandeliers can be heavy

Carved wood
An energetic whirligig of fine carving, the extrovert shape is belied by the discreet gesso-like paint finish — a design that harks back to scrolled and foliated Chippendale designs.

Stylized leaf applied to the basic structure

Ornate metal
A festive and light-hearted chandelier, this basically simple construction is enriched by a handful of applied leaves. The finish is in verdigris, delicately gilded and distressed, giving it an appropriate autumnal warmth.

Decorative scrolls are added once the main rod is shaped

Crown of lights
A modern interpretation of the medieval corona chandelier, this has a subverted recollection of the original prickets. The texture of wrought iron is lost with paint — beeswax and turpentine prevent rust and enhance the natural character of the metal.

Accessories

Once a passion for candles has been kindled, you will find that there are all sorts of adjuncts to make them burn more prettily, and ingenious ideas intended to make them behave better. Safety is also a consideration that must not be forgotten, and to this end there are gadgets that help to keep candles stable and upright, and snuffers to ensure that an extinguished flame really is dead. And some things – shades or antique wick trimmers, for example – are desirable simply for the aesthetic pleasure that they bring.

Drip catchers
An indispensable aid to cleaning, these protect surfaces from hot wax.

Boldly striped pleated paper shade

Integral snuffer

Gilded swags on a navy enamelled shade

Shade holders
These either grip the candle with a spring, or slide over the top of the candle like a hood. They hold the shade at a constant height over the flame as the candle burns down.

Candle shades (left)
Much used in Edwardian times, shades give a dim but elegant illumination.

Antique brass snuffer

Reproduction snuffer of wrought iron

An elegant silver and
ebony snuffer

Snuffers
These douse the flame effectively and obviate
some of the smell of extinguished candles.

**Christmas
tree holders**
These grip the branches
like clothes pegs.

Box to collect the
spent wick

Wick trimmer
Modern plaited wicks need less attention
than the twisted wicks of the past, so
a trimmer is no longer a necessity.

Candle boxes
Storage boxes hung on the wall
meant that candles could
always be found, and it
was obvious when
supplies were
running low.

Candle stickers
Purpose-made discs of wax
hold the candle firmly in place.

Foam snuggers
Thin discs of foam grip the
candle in its holder. Once pressed
into position, they are not visible.

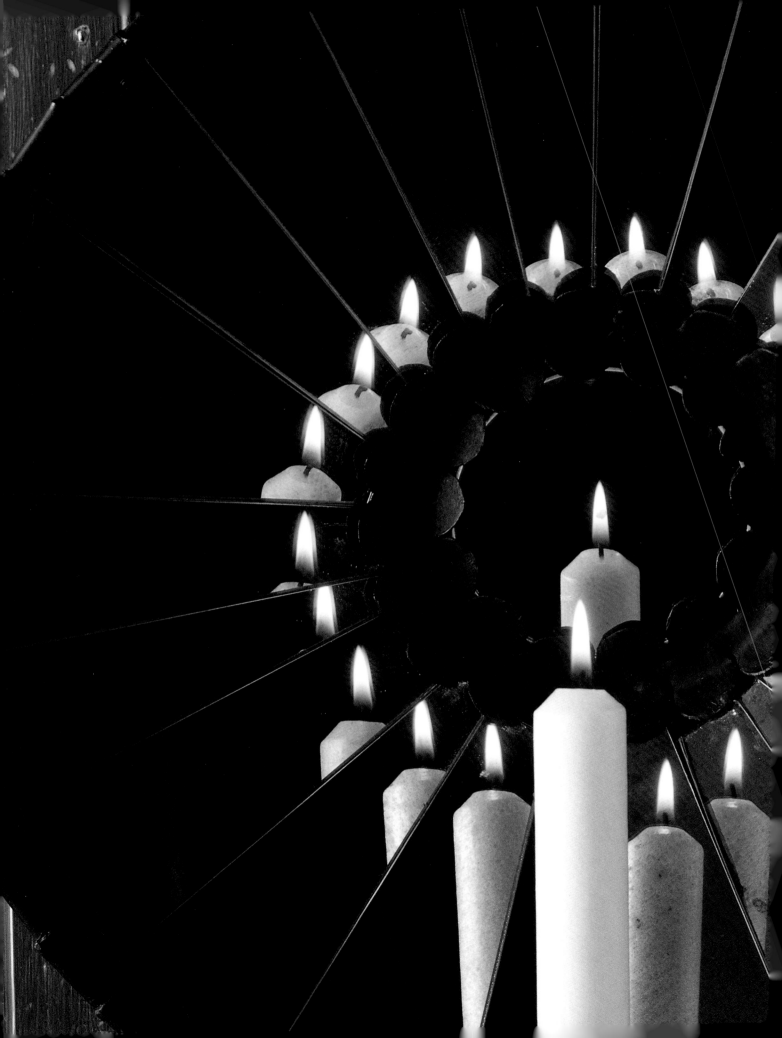

DECORATING WITH CANDLES

Light is the most important
decorative element in any room,
and candlelight has an unrivalled
evocative power, warming
colours, creating a charmed
circle of interest, and benignly
censoring the ugly banalities
of life. Whatever the setting,
here are ideas and inspiration
for candlelit interiors to
suit any mood.

Christmas in the city

Dark, rich, baroque colours characterize Christmas in the city. The classic combination of red, green and gold makes a festive theme upon which to play variations – here, an air of sophistication and opulence is apposite, taking the three kings rather than the manger as your cue. Fortunately, the jewels do not need to be real, and frankincense and myrrh can impart fragrance to candles rather than grace priceless coffers – an enjoyment of the theatrical is all part of this look, and an element of kitsch is not out of place. A city Christmas looks to Renaissance Italy for inspiration, with the glowing brocades, intricate jewels and dark shadows of paintings by Bellini and Titian. Go for rich, strong colours combined with glossy evergreens and a glitter of golden ornaments. For a look of sumptuous luxury, light rooms entirely by candles, with hosts of matching or theme-related candlesticks.

Baroque table-top (left) *Gilded putti, and a cornucopia of wine-dark fruit – this is a Bacchanalian interpretation of Christmas with strong Roman antecedents.*

Glittering mantelpiece (right) *A dazzle of golden candlesticks, rich reflections in a gilded mirror, and a fat swag of beribboned evergreens – these are the ingredients for a city celebration, making a defiant blaze of brightness at the very darkest time of the year.*

Christmas in the country

Simple, casual, natural – these are the words that characterize a country Christmas. The soft, subtle colours beloved of the Scandinavians – verdigris, russet and ivory – work well with rough plaster and scrubbed wood, while the sort of tasteful sobriety that came easily to the Shakers has a natural affinity with bone-white and beeswax candles. This is an innocent Christmas, the peaceful antidote to parties, hangovers, glitter and baubles. The ingredients are probably in front of you in wood and hedgerow, embellished very simply with terracotta plant pots and twine from your garden, spices and pomanders from your kitchen, and ribbons from your workbox. Keep to uncluttered arrangements in muted colours, with a variety of natural textures to lend interest and the subtle light of candles adding a sympathetic glow.

Advent wreath (above)
A ring of oasis, crammed with the remnants of autumn richness — berries, mosses, bark and pine cones — makes a sympathetic roosting place for four Advent candles, one to be burned on each of the four Sundays to Christmas.

Cottage simplicity (right)
Verdigris metal is a kindly partner to bowls and baskets of reindeer moss in which lie chunky ivory candles. This pretty Scandinavian custom is perfect for table centres and window sills.

Country cottage style

The natural materials and simple finishes of cottage style lend themselves to the gentle glow of candlelight: plain cream dipped candles and fragrant ochre beeswax are ideal partners to wood and rough plaster. There is a warmth and liveliness in candlelight that perfectly suits irregular or textured walls and weathered, functional furniture. The small focus of a candle flame is kind to country clutter, fading old wellington boots and dog baskets into benign obscurity, while glancing brightly on china-filled dressers and sparkling glass. The fragile flame defies whatever weather rages outside, drawing attention inwards to safe cosiness. The friendly customs of northern Europe – windows lined with lights to signify welcome to the passing stranger, or seasonal celebration to the world at large – can be rekindled in darkest Devon.

The Shaker tradition
(left and below)
The Shakers achieved the perfect marriage of form and function, producing everyday objects of natural grace and simplicity. Typical is painted wood in a muted colour paired with a sculptural minimalism of metal.

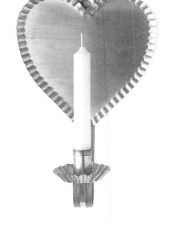

A country dresser (right)
A more eclectic interpretation of country living is given by masses of beeswax candles and rustic candlesticks of turned and painted wood, verdigris metal, and an insouciant fox prancing among earthy painted pottery.

Romantic style

Candles are synonymous with romance – their soft, glowing light transforms the most practical workaday interior with warmth and mystery. There is something about the little halo of candlelight that draws people together in conspiratorial closeness and focuses attention on the niceties – the glittering ensemble of glass, silver and porcelain. Scented candles add to a general feeling of luxury – choose rich, heady fragrances such as rose, jasmine or orchid, or the earthy wood scents of cedar or sandalwood. This is the opportunity to use your best china and finest tableware with plenty of muted antique gilt. A tureen of floating candles illuminates food and faces at a flattering height. For a side table or in a bedroom, introduce a touch of nostalgia with artless Victoriana and drifts of white lace.

Dinner table (left)
Dancing flames reflected in a wall of stars –
cherubs support a dish of floating candles,
and a fringe of glass beads diffuses the light.

Lacy bedroom (above)
An utterly romantic table – posies, bows and
family mementos. White candles add dignity
to what could be an excess of sweetness.

Classic perfection

The ultimate in refinement, classic style is a considered look: nothing happens by chance, and good things tend to be symmetrical and come in pairs. Silver, elegant fluted columns of gilt, porphyry, marble – the materials to look for are solid, valuable, and improved by the patina of time. Ideally, the candlesticks are left to you with the estate, but failing such good management, it is possible to find affordable antiques, occasional fakes, or even to emulate marble and lapis lazuli yourself on a plain wooden candlestick. The rich, dark colours of a gentlemen's club suit the style, as do the surprising bright colours favoured by Robert Adam. Pillars, plinths, gryphons, obelisks, Georgian candelabra with sinuous S-shaped arms and second empire laurel wreaths are all motifs to look for, and are appropriate partners to ornate gilt picture frames, an old master or two, or a crisp and architectural Palladian print.

Studied formality (left)
Symmetry is all: a somewhat heterogeneous ensemble of metal candle-sticks, none of which is entirely classical, takes on a convincing air of the antique when arranged with punctilious and formal symmetry. Dark wallpaper and a polished 18th-century table help.

Architectural echoes (above)
Grouped in front of a wall of *Adam-ish* blue, this collection of pillars and obelisks, plus a silver candelabra, has a clean sobriety. This sort of classical reference works well with the architectural print, and is shown off by the sculptural swags of a muslin tablecloth.

Ethnic styles

Indigo and spice colours, hand-made objects proclaiming their peculiarities, extrovert shapes and finishes — ethnic is a vigorous antidote to the clinical perfections of our machine-made world of high-technology. The very presence of a finely made African basket, or a carved and painted Indian elephant seems mutely to encourage slowing down and reverting to the simpler pleasures. The rich exuberance of Africa and India; the brilliant colours and relish in kitsch, painted tin and rainbow textiles that characterize South American style; the sobriety of Chinese lacquer and delicate basketwork; the carelessly hand-painted roses glowing from a dark background beloved of the Russians — these are all expressions of ethnic international folk art. Go for the spirit of the look, rather than slavish authenticity — you are trying to create a mood, not a museum. Be bold with your candles — massive cream church candles always look good, but experiment with bright colours and adventurous shapes.

Indian look (above)
Rich colours and patterns — paisley motifs, tiny flowers, exuberant saffron yellow and cinnabar red — complement the solidity of carved wooden candlesticks and the vigorous simplicity of the Divali screen, the multi-level sconce essential to the festival of lights.

African look (right)
A block-printed pale indigo hanging makes a sympathetic backdrop to carved ebony candlesticks and a well-made Ali Baba basket. The massive black spiral candlestick gives scale and contrast to a collection of intricately carved wood and naive wrought metal.

A contemporary look

From the kitsch charms of tinsel or the casual brightness of a touch of peasant ethnic, to the expensive hand-made designer original, this is a look where anything goes. Electric clean colours make dramatic partnerships: use strongly dyed bright primary candles in simple shapes against a bold background. Or go for a more spartan style: geometric candles are the ideal match to a minimalist interior – spheres, pyramids, cubes and cones – and there is a wide range of shapes in black, white, cream or grey which will complement severe monochrome interiors. Contemporary style is about having fun and trying daring contrasts. The vital accessory that can give life to an interior, a candle is not, after all, a major investment, so you can experiment with the whole spectrum of colours and every kind of shape and size.

Modern medieval (left)
Light-hearted stripy arabesques cavort on this handmade wool rug, and make a lively background to simple wrought iron candlesticks holding unashamedly clashing candles.

International glitter (above)
The irreverent wit of contemporary design from London and Mexico. The mirror sconce is covered in a magpie's hoard of bright bits and pieces, and is comfortably at home with ethnic tin candlesticks.

THE ART
OF MAKING
CANDLES

Simple ingredients for a
satisfying sense of achievement –
even the raw materials have an
earthy charm. Candle-making is
fun: the rules are there to be
broken, failures are not tragic and
experimentation is part of the
pleasure. You can always burn
your flawed masterpiece, and it
will glow just as brightly. Here
are straightforward instructions
for making and decorating your
own candles.

Preparing to make candles

Making your own candles is straight-forward, does not require complicated equipment, and gives a wonderful sense of achievement for very little cost or effort. It also gives you a chance to produce exactly the effects you want, to make unusual shapes, and to create a range of subtle colours which look marvellous together and which are custom-made for your decoration and candlesticks.

BASIC EQUIPMENT
Cooker or **hotplate**
Scales
Double boiler or any tall heatproof container in a pan of hot water
Newspaper and **apron**
Specific methods of candle-making may need additional equipment (see equipment listed under each method).

USEFUL INFORMATION
• 1 tbsp wax weighs about 25g (1oz)
• 1 litre (1³/₄pts) volume = 900g (2lb) solid wax
• 3kg (6¹/₂lb) wax makes 6 candles 12-19mm (¹/₂-³/₄in) diameter and 22.5cm (9in) long
• A container 30cm deep by 20cm wide (12 x 8in) will take 7kg (15lb) wax

Wax thermometer
This covers a lower temperature range than an ordinary cooking thermometer.

TYPES OF WAX

Paraffin wax
The basic wax used in candle-making, this is cheap and easy to work. It comes as tiny beads or pellets.

Beeswax
This is more expensive and harder to work with than paraffin wax, but a small amount can be mixed with paraffin wax to improve the quality of the candle.

Wax sheets
These are available in both beeswax and paraffin wax. Beeswax sheets often come with a honeycomb texture.

Stearin
A little is added to wax to prevent candles dripping excessively. It also makes the wax opaque, helps to distribute dyes and makes candles easier to remove from moulds.

WICKS

It is important to use the correct size of wick for the thickness of candle you are making: too thick and the candle will smoke, too thin and the candle will burn with too small a flame, and may go out. The sizes correspond to the diameter of a candle made of paraffin wax with up to 10 per cent beeswax content: pure beeswax candles need a thicker wick.

DYES

When dyeing wax, bear in mind that the colour changes as it cools. Check the final colour by putting about a teaspoonful of the dyed wax in a shallow container and leaving it to cool for about five minutes. Then, if necessary, strengthen the colour by adding dye or dilute by adding wax.

Plaited cotton wicks
Wicks for candles from 12.5mm (½in) to 76mm (3in) thick.

Purpose-made dyes
Available as powder or in blocks, these distribute quickly and easily through the wax.

Wax crayons
Grate or crumble these into wax.

Oil paints
Blend these to achieve subtle colours.

Fabric dye sticks
These will dissolve if grated or crumbled into wax.

GENERAL TIPS

Melting wax
Always melt wax in a container over a pan of hot water. To blend waxes and dye, melt the stearin, then add the dye and stir it in. When both have melted, add the wax, stirring as it melts. Use a thermometer to check the temperature of the wax.

Using beeswax
Beeswax is viscous and tends to stick to the mould, so use up to 10 per cent beeswax or add a silicon-releasing agent to help remove the candle from its mould. For any beeswax candle, whether moulded, dipped or rolled, use a thicker wick than usual.

Priming the wick
For good results, prime the wicks before making candles. Melt a little wax and immerse the wicks for about five minutes, then take them out and pull them straight. Lay them on greaseproof paper to harden.

General precautions
• Keep unused wax clean, so that candles you make later don't have dust or fluff in them.
• Never dispose of melted wax down the drain.
• Never leave wax to set in a container with a base wider than the top, since when you remelt, the wax can spurt out violently.
• If wax begins to smoke, switch off the heat, but do not touch the wax. If it catches fire, smother the flames with a lid.

Making dipped candles

A gratifyingly simple procedure, dipping requires only basic ingredients and a modicum of patience. You will need a container deeper than the height of the finished candle, which necessitates a huge volume of wax – a container 30cm (12in) deep by 20cm (8in) wide will hold about 7kg (15lb) of wax. Beeswax is expensive to use in such quantities, but paraffin wax is more affordable. Dipped candles are usually made in pairs: but beware, the candles in a pair have a fatal predilection for each other – if they can weld together, they will, so you may find it easier to make candles singly at first. Dipping is a time-consuming process, so it is a good idea to make a batch of three or four individual candles or pairs at a time.

You will need
About 1.4kg (3lb) stearin (optional)
¹/₈ disc of dye (optional)
About 7kg (15lb) paraffin wax, more if your container is over 20cm (8in) in diameter
350g (³/₄lb) beeswax (optional)
Four 60cm (24in) lengths of 12.5mm wick
Double boiler or dipping can, at least 30cm (12in) tall
Wax thermometer
Spoon or stick for stirring
Tall container of cold water
Hooks or a rod for hanging candles to dry
Newspaper or bowl to catch drips

1 Heat the stearin, stirring it as it melts, then add the dye, if you are using it. Add the wax to a depth of about 25cm (10in) and heat to 71°C (160°F), stirring as it melts. Prime the wicks (see page 65).

2 Hold the wick in the middle and dip the two ends into the wax to a depth of about 25cm (10in), with a swift, smooth movement, leaving a clear area of about 10cm (4in) at the middle.

3 Dip the wick in cold water to cool it, then hang it up to dry, making sure that the ends do not touch. Dip the remaining wicks in wax, then water.

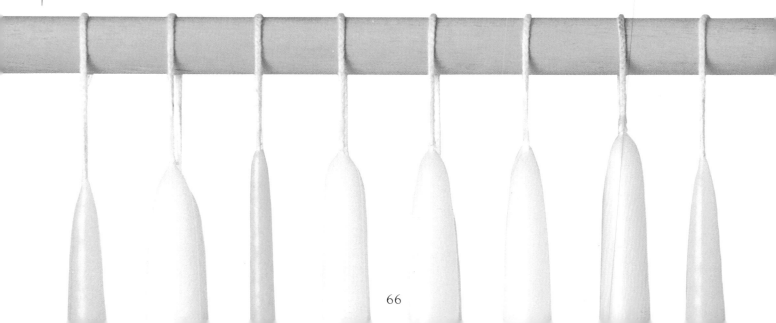

4 Continue dipping the candles in the wax followed by water, leaving them to dry for about a minute between each dip, until they are the desired thickness. They will probably need at least 20 dips.

5 Heat the wax to 82°C (180°F) and dip each pair of candles twice for three seconds, allowing them to cool for a minute in between, to give a smooth finish. Leave for at least an hour before burning.

OVERDIPPING IN COLOUR

White candles can be overdipped in an outer coating of coloured wax. Coated candles have a more intense colour than solid-colour candles, and do not fade as quickly. To overdip, melt a little dye and wax together and heat a deep pan of water almost to boiling point. Pour the wax slowly on to the hot water to prevent bubbles forming in the floating wax, as they have an unattractive similarity to acne on a candle. Hold the candles by the wick and dip them up to the wick. Let them cool, then repeat until you obtain the colour you desire.

STRIPED CANDLES

For a striped candle with four bands of colour, heat four pans of water and float wax and dye in different colours, ranging from light to dark, in each pan. Dip the candle twice in the lightest colour up to the wick, allowing it to dry between each dip. Next, dip it twice in the second palest colour to about three quarters of its length, letting it dry between dips. Then dip it twice in the third colour to half its length, and finally dip it in the darkest colour to a quarter of its length.

Striped candles with six bands of colour

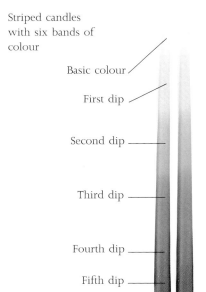

Basic colour

First dip

Second dip

Third dip

Fourth dip

Fifth dip

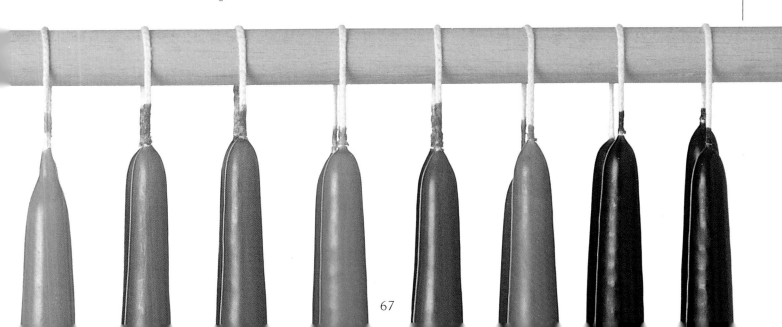

Making moulded candles

Made by pouring molten wax into a prepared container, moulded candles are straight-forward to make. Candle-makers supply shops sell moulds in glass, plastic, rubber or metal, some in shapes such as spheres, which come apart in the middle to release the candle. Once you start thinking along the candle-making lines, you will find all sorts of possibilities – metal dariole and petits fours moulds, for example, offer interesting shapes and sizes. Candle wax has an amazing ability to pick up the minutest imperfection on the surface of a mould, so unless the mould is perfectly smooth, brush cooking oil over the inside.

You will need
25g (1oz) stearin (not for a rubber mould)
1/8 disc of dye (optional)
225g (7oz) paraffin wax
50mm wick, 40cm (16in) long
Wax thermometer
Double boiler (or saucepan and container)
Spoon or stick for stirring
Mould
Cooking oil and brush (optional)
Mould seal (or chewing gum or Plasticine)
Pencil or small knitting needle
Cardboard
Scissors
Deep container of cold water

1 Heat the stearin. When it has melted, add the dye and stir until they have blended thoroughly.

2 Add 11 tablespoons of paraffin wax, and leave the mixture to melt, stirring occasionally. Prime the wicks (see page 65). Put the thermometer into the wax.

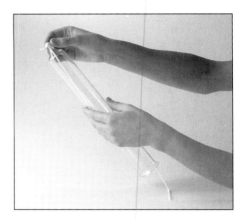

3 Lightly oil the mould, if necessary, then thread the wick through the hole at the base, and cover it with enough mould seal to make a watertight seal.

4 Pull the wick taut and tie the loose end to a pencil or knitting needle, to hold it in place down the centre of the mould. Cut a cardboard collar to hold the mould upright in the container of cold water.

5 When the wax reaches 82°C (180°F), pour it carefully into the mould, trickling it down the side to prevent it frothing up. After a minute or two, tap the mould on the side to release any air bubbles.

6 Place the mould in a deep container of cold water to cool the wax, making sure that no water splashes into the wax. Hold the mould vertical with the cardboard collar.

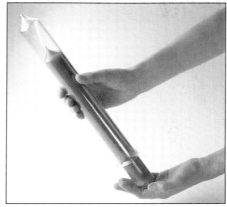

7 *The wax shrinks as it cools, and after about an hour there will be a well around the wick at the top. Pierce the surface film, and top up the well with molten wax, being careful not to flood over on to the surrounding solidified wax.*

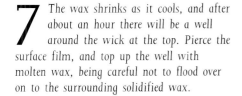

8 *When the candle has set, take the mould out of the water and remove the seal. Hold the mould upside down and let the candle slide out. Trim the wick, then level the base of the candle by holding it briefly against the base of a heated saucepan.*

USING OTHER TYPES OF MOULD

Look around catering equipment shops for containers to use as moulds: you can use anything provided it will withstand hot wax and that it is wider at the top than at the base, so that the candle can slide out when set. If you can make a small hole in the base to accommodate the wick, so much the better. If not, use a wicking needle longer than the height of your candle to thread the wick through the candle when it is set.

To use a rubber mould, melt the wax and dye together, but don't use stearin, since it rots the rubber. As the candle sets, break the surface skin of the wax frequently and top up with molten wax after about two hours. To remove it from the mould, smear washing up liquid over the outside and peel the mould back carefully.

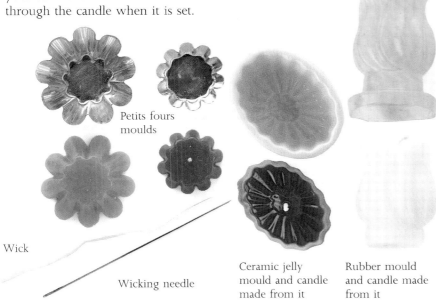

Petits fours moulds

Wick

Wicking needle

Ceramic jelly mould and candle made from it

Rubber mould and candle made from it

Glass mould

Making rolled candles

Rolled candles are the easiest of all to make and may not even require a heat-source, which means that children can make their own candles. A thin sheet of wax is simply rolled up round a wick. Sheets of beeswax are the easiest to work with – they are generally tan-coloured, with a honeycomb texture. Paraffin wax is less malleable than beeswax, so you may need to warm the sheet first to avoid cracking it when you roll it. To warm it, leave it on top of a radiator or in a very low oven for a few minutes, or carefully play a hair dryer over it until the wax softens.

You will need
Scissors or blade and ruler
1 sheet of beeswax or
1 sheet of paraffin wax 2–3mm thick
12mm wick, 20cm (8in) long

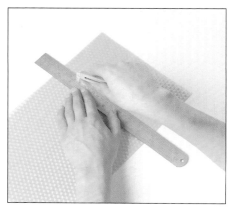

1 Cut the wax into a rectangle. The length of the short sides will be the height of your candle, while that of the long sides determines its thickness.

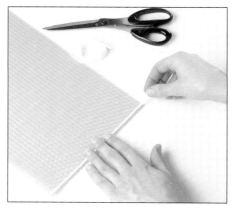

2 Cut the wick 2cm (1in) longer than the narrow side of the wax rectangle and gently press it into the wax along one of the short sides.

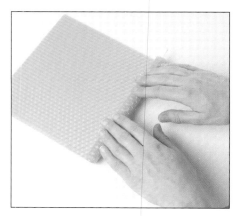

3 Roll up the wax tightly to enclose the wick in the middle. Ensure that the wick is closely and evenly held with the first turn. The more tightly you roll, the longer the candle will burn.

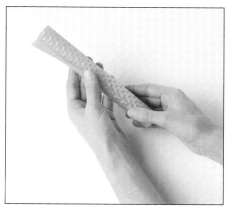

4 When the candle is the thickness you want, cut off any surplus wax parallel to the wick using scissors or a blade and ruler. Press the cut edge into the roll to give a neat finish.

SPIRAL CANDLES
Make a spiral candle by cutting the sheet of wax into a triangle. Trim a tiny amount from the corner that will form the top of the candle, then place the wick along the edge and roll the wax as before. A tall narrow triangle will give a tall spiral candle, while a broad triangle will produce a conical one.

Rolled candle

Spiral candles

Making scented candles

One of the pleasures of making your own candles is that of imparting a delicious fragrance to the room when they burn. Any shop that sells candle supplies will have a range of special scented oils with which you can concoct the perfect scent. According to aromatherapists, smells can soothe or revitalize – certainly sensuous wafts of sandalwood or a refreshing whiff of lavender promote a feeling of well-being. In addition, the scent of citronella has useful mosquito and midge deterrent qualities, which could prevent you from being insect-food when enjoying a candlelit dinner outside. There are four ways of scenting candles, all very simple – it is worth the little additional effort to add extra cachet to your candles.

You will need
Candle scents or essential oils or herbs or aromatic flowers

Candle scents

Oil of juniper

Lavender flowers

Lemon verbena leaves

QUICK METHOD
The easiest way of adding scent to a candle is simply to put a few drops of scented oil around the burning wick – an effect that will not last long, but will give a powerful burst of fragrance.

SCENTING THE WICK
For a reasonably long-lasting fragrance, melt a little wax and add a few drops of scent. Prime a handful of wicks (*see page 65*) in this for about 20 minutes, then make candles using any of the techniques described on pages 66 to 70.

SCENTING THE WAX
For the most enduring scent, impregnate the wax as you make the candles. Melt the wax and stearin (*see page 65*), then add a few drops of scent – nine or ten drops to a kilo is enough, more may mottle the candles. Blend the mixture well, then dip or mould the candles as usual.

USING HERBS AND FLOWERS
Dried and fresh herbs and flowers macerated in molten wax release a slight fragrance as they burn, which can be heightened by adding a few drops of matching scent. Melt wax and stearin, then add a bunch of herbs and leave for 45 minutes, keeping the temperature to about 75°C (180°F). Remove the herbs, add a little scent if desired, and make candles by dipping or moulding.

Jasmine scented candle

Rose scented candle

Dropper for scents and oils

Pressed flower candles

With a steady hand and a little patience, the flowers of summer can be pressed and then set on to candles to bloom again long after the first frosts. Collect your plant material when it is fresh and open, before there is any hint of drooping petals, and make sure that it is dry and free of insects. Use a flower press, or place each item face down on two layers of tissue or blotting paper laid smoothly between the pages of a hefty book. Restrict yourself to one type of plant per sheet, and make sure that the flowers or leaves do not overlap or they will stick to each other. Flatten the flowers slightly with your fingers, and top with another two pieces of tissue. Shut the book gently, put another on top, and leave for at least a week. It takes very little practice to become proficient at decorating candles with pressed flowers. Large round and square pillar candles are the easiest to handle, and a simple pressed garland around the base will be enough for you to master the technique.

You will need
Teaspoon
Iron or hotplate
Selection of pressed flowers and leaves
Tissue paper
White pillar candle
Cloth or non-roll surface
Tweezers
For overdipping: Double boiler (or saucepan and container), 1kg (2lb) paraffin wax, spoon or stick for stirring, 2-3 drops of candle scent (optional), pliers

1 Heat the paraffin wax gently over a saucepan of hot water, stirring occasionally, until it has melted.

2 Add the candle scent if you want to scent the candles as you dip them. Meanwhile, heat up the bowl of a teaspoon on an iron or hotplate.

3 Arrange the pressed flowers on a sheet of tissue paper to give an idea of the finished design. Lay the candle on a cloth and carefully position one of the larger elements against the side of the candle.

4 Delicately press all parts of the flower on to the candle with the heated spoon, rolling it gently over the surface of the flower.

5 Carefully build up your design one item at a time, positioning each flower or leaf accurately, then ironing gently over it with the heated spoon to fix it in place with melted wax.

6 Once the arrangement is complete, seal the candle by overdipping it. Hold it firmly by the wick — you may need pliers if the wick is short — and immerse it in the hot wax.

7 Lift the candle out after about three seconds and allow it to dry. Leave it for at least an hour before burning it.

Floral diversity
Delicately coloured and graphic in shape, pressed flowers embellish candles with pleasing effects, from a geometric trellis pattern to naturalistic garlands.

Painting techniques

For a special occasion, or to suit a very splendid candlestick, it is surprisingly easy to decorate candles. Bold designs can be applied with stencils – numerals for a birthday candle, snowflakes and stars on a Christmas candle, hearts and even initials for St. Valentine's day. Roman numerals and horizontal stripes, guided with masking tape, make an effective but not too accurate medieval time-piece. Sponging with layers of colour is quick and easy and makes for subtle cloudy shades and textures. A veil of gold sponged on the top looks rich and festive. It is simplest to work on a stout white candle using poster paint or gouache.

STENCILLING

1 Stick one edge of a stencil to the candle with masking tape. Pull the stencil round the candle to ensure a snug fit, then tape down the other side.

2 Mix the paint with water and a drop or two of washing up liquid, to the consistency of thick cream. Dab on a fine layer of colour with a cosmetic sponge.

3 If the base colour lacks subtlety or depth, or if you want to highlight particular areas or outlines, dab on a toning or contrasting colour.

4 When the paint is completely dry, peel off the masking tape and carefully remove the stencil. Avoid touching the painted area, and seal the design by over-dipping (see page 73, steps 6-7).

Strong, bold shapes are typical of stencilled patterns.

Stencilled pattern

SPONGING

Use gold paint for the third coat on a sponged candle to achieve something positively baroque.

1 Mix paint with a little water and washing up liquid, and dab colour lightly over the sides and top of the candle with a sponge. Avoid getting paint on the wick.

2 When the first colour is dry, repeat the process with a toning colour. Add a third colour for extra richness. Overdip in paraffin wax (see page 73, steps 6-7).

FREEHAND PAINTING

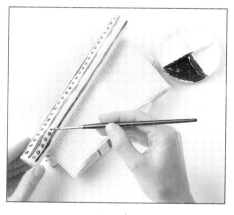

Take inspiration from ceramics, fabrics or wall-paper patterns. Bold irregular peasant designs are easier than crisp Chippendale.

Freehand painting

Gold stippling

Freehand dots and stripes

Mix paint with a little water and washing up liquid to the consistency of thin cream, and with a medium-sized artist's brush, paint all over the candle. Overdip in paraffin wax (see page 73, steps 6-7).

Rhythmic, fluent painting looks good.

Freehand design

Freehand stripes and zigzags

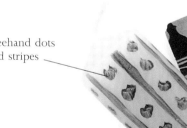

Mixed media

Generally, the simpler a candle the better, but there are times when a fit of creativity demands something a little more decorative, and a candle is a compliant sculptural medium for experimentation. It is salutary to remember that you are not creating a permanent work of art, so that your inspiration need be only a passing whim or fanciful idea. Watch flammable materials vigilantly, and avoid anything likely to give off toxic fumes. With thicker candles, only the wick area burns, and your designs may glow with the flame like stained glass.

You will need
Fresh foliage: Leaves, pins, raffia, flowers
Carving: Equipment, wax and dye for overdipping; lino cutting tool, paint, washing up liquid, fine paint brush
Foil: Coloured foil or metallic paper, scissors, teaspoon, iron or hotplate, sequins, pins or glue
Tissue: Tissue paper, printer's block and ink pad, teaspoon, iron or hotplate; equipment and wax for overdipping

FRESH FOLIAGE

1 Select a few unblemished ivy leaves and pin them in position round the base of a thick candle. Skeleton leaves also look very pretty.

2 Wrap some raffia round the candle to hold the leaves in place, tie it in a bow, then remove the pins. Tuck a tiny posy of flowers into the raffia.

A festive and ephemeral confection of ivy, raffia and *Chaenomeles*.

CARVING

1 Dip a candle in wax of a strong, contrasting colour floating on hot water (see page 67), to get a deep, smooth overlay. Allow the wax to cool completely.

2 Using a lino cutting tool, carefully chisel out stars all over the candle, carving through the outer coating of wax to reveal the colour beneath.

3 For a festive touch, mix a little gold paint with water and a drop of washing up liquid, and paint each star gold using a fine paint brush.

APPLYING FOIL

A magpie's collection of metallic paper and sequins is perfect for Hallowe'en or a kitsch Christmas.

1 Cut shapes of coloured foil or metallic paper — bold geometric shapes are easiest to begin with.

2 Heat a teaspoon against an iron or hotplate, position each piece of foil and press it in place with the hot spoon. Finally, glue or pin on a few sequins.

APPLYING TISSUE PAPER

Carved stripes

White tissue paper becomes transparent when overdipped.

1 Cut tissue paper to fit round your candle. Use ready-patterned paper, or decorate your own — here a pattern is stamped with a printer's block.

2 Heat a teaspoon against an iron or hotplate, then wrap the tissue round the candle and iron over it with the spoon. Seal by overdipping (see page 73, steps 6-7).

Strips of coloured tissue paper

Carved shapes can be painted or left so that the base colour shows through.

Carved and painted stars

Patterned paper

Carved decorations

List of suppliers

Candle specialists

The Candle Shop
30 The Market
Covent Garden
London WC2
071-836 9815
Candles and candlesticks

Candlewick Green
Neal Street
London WC2
071-497 8956/680 3688
Candles and candlesticks

Dansk Import
5 Gunton Cliff
Lowestoft
Suffolk NR32 4PE
0502 573675
Mail order candles

Fly by Night
17 Hill Way
Linton
Cambs CB1 6JR
0223 892785
Hand-made candles

Price's Candles
110 York Road
London SW11 3RU
071-228 3345
Candle manufacturer, supplies many shops

Candlestick suppliers

Acres Farm
Bradfield
Nr Reading
Berks RG7 6JH
0743 744305
Candlesticks and shades

Anne's &
Kensington Lighting Company
34 & 59 Kensington Church St.
London W8 4HA
071-937 5033/938 2405
Chandeliers and candlesticks

Artisan
797 Wandsworth Road
London SW8 3JT
071-498 6974
Designer candlesticks

Barclay and Bodie
7 Blenheim Crescent
London NW8
071-328 7879/372 5705
Metal candlesticks, sconces

Mary Bellis Antiques
Hungerford
Berkshire
0488 682 620
Antique candlesticks

Carless & Grey
608 King's Road
London SW6
071-731 3837
Antique and reproduction candlesticks and sconces

The Conran Shop
Michelin House
81 Fulham Road
London SW3
071-589 7401
Modern and ethnic candlesticks, candles

Contemporary Applied Arts
43 Earlham Street
London WC2H 9LD
071-836 6993
Designer candlesticks

Craft Centre
Royal Exchange Theatre
St. Anne's Square
Manchester M2 7DH
061-833 9333
Designer candlesticks

Davies
10 Great Newport Street
London WC2
071-240 2223
Metal candlesticks, church and beeswax candles

Deeva
819 Fulham Road
London SW6
071-371 5899
Old Divali lamps

The Dining Room Shop
62-64 White Hart Lane
London SW13 0PZ
081-878 1020
Candlesticks, shades

Freud
198 Shaftsbury Avenue
London WC2
071-831 1071
Modern candlesticks, candles

Freya Lighting
94 Sandpiper Road
Ipswich
Suffolk IP2 9HT
0473 687258/86238
Wooden candlesticks

General Trading Company
144 Sloane Street
London SW1
071-730 1411
Traditional, ethnic and contemporary candlesticks

Global Village Crafts
Sparrow Works
Bower Hinton
Martock
Somerset TA12 6LG
0935 823390
Ethnic candlesticks

Thomas Goode
19 South Audley Street
London W1
071-499 0411
Classic candlesticks

Gore Booker
41 Bedford Street
London WC2R 9HA
071-497 1254
Candlesticks

Graham and Green
4&7 Elgin Crescent
London W11
071-727 4594
Sconces, metal candlesticks

Inca
29-30 Kingly Street
London W1R 5LB
071-730 7941
Ethnic tin candlesticks

McCloud & Co
61 Hillier Street
London SW11
071-350 1448
Designer candlesticks, sconces and chandeliers

Mexique
97 Sheen Lane
London SW14 8AD
081-392 2345
Ethnic candlesticks

New World Trading Co
King's Langley
Hertfordshire
0923 269527
Tin lanterns, angel lamps

One World Trading
9a Studio Centre
Ranelagh Gardens
London SW6 3PA
071-381 1111
African candles and candlesticks

Jane Packer
56 James Street
London W1
071-935 2673
Scented candles

Peepul Tree Trading
291 New Kings Road
London SW6 4RE
071-736 9132
Designer candlesticks

The Study Shop
55 Endell Street
London WC2H 9AJ
071-379 9303
Designer candlesticks

Woolpit Interiors
Woolpit
Bury St. Edmunds
Suffolk IP30 9SA
0359 40895
Painted wooden candlesticks

Verandah
15 Blenheim Crescent
London W11
071-792 9289
Ethnic candlesticks and lanterns

Candle-making equipment

Candle Makers Supplies
28 Blythe Road
London W14 0PP
081-602 4031/1812
Equipment and materials for making candles

Index

Acknowledgments

Dorling Kindersley would like to thank Karen Ward for design help, Karl Adamson for photographic assistance, Hilary Bird for the index, and all staff who kindly lent candlesticks for photography.

We are particularly grateful to the following people for their help in supplying props for photography: Pauline Sherman, Glynn Lowe and Stephanie Thomson at Candlewick Green, Chris Ryan and Louis Spear at The Candle Shop, Nick Gaiger at Nice Irma's and Saira Joshi at Thomas Goode.

Other suppliers who lent props include: Acres Farm, Anne's, J. Bostock & Associates, Candle Makers Supplies, Carless & Grey, Casa Pupo, The Conran Shop, Davies, Designer's Guild, Divine Lights, Fergus Cochrane, The General Trading Company, Global Village, Gore Booker, Judy Greenwood, Habitat, Mexique, Molton Brown, Neal Street East, Overmantels, Jane Packer, Peepul Tree Trading, Perfect Glass Shop, Prices

Candles, R. G. Scrutton, The Shaker Shop, The Study, Kenneth Turner, Verandah, Keith Watson, Ann Wood, Steve Wright, Zawadi.

Stylist for pages 52-61: Cherry Frost.

Film setting
The Setting Studio, Newcastle.

Picture credits
Key: t = top; b = bottom
The National Gallery, 6, 7t; Fine Art Photographs, 7b; The Mansell Collection, 8t; Prices Candles, 8b; The Tate Gallery, 9.

Author's acknowledgments
I would like to thank Clive Streeter and Karl Adamson for their patient ingenuity and ability to create sunshine with a lightbulb, Daphne and Anne-Marie who kept hope glowing in darker moments, Claire for her competence with both words and wax, and Sarah, who juggled successfully with the look of it all. Many people waxed lyrical and enlightening along the way – particularly Daphne Dormer, George Carter, Bridget Bodoano at Conran, Nana Laye at Dansk Import, Katya Dumonde, Steve Wright and Jane Packer. David Constable at Candle Makers Supplies made me watch a most illuminating video, the people at The Candle Shop, and Pauline Sherman at Candlewick Green shed what light they could. And Hester Page at Country Living burned the candle at both ends in a characteristic effort to lighten one's darkness.